EIGHT DAYS UNDER

A story of surviving COVID

Published in Savannah, Georgia by Marigold Press Books, a division of International School of Story.

Marigold Press Books titles may be purchased in bulk for educational, business, fund-raising, or sales promotional use. For information, please email marigoldpressbooks@gmail.com.

Fonts and stock images licensed for commercial use.

Library of Congress Control Number: 2023906613

ISBN: 9781942923602

Cover Design by Rebekah McLeod

Fonts licensed for use.

EIGHT DAYS UNDER

A story of surviving COVID

Dr. Sage Campione, DC

Dedication

My, have I grown. Just when you think you're already grown and have matured, something tragic happens and you grow again.

This book is dedicated to my husband, Darrell, who helped me by being my coach, nurse, spouse, best friend, and protector.

To my pastors, David and Justin. Pastor David was like velcro—he stuck to our family through it all. Justin was the one with boots on the ground rallying prayer warriors to see me through. I am forever grateful. You both will always have a special place in my heart.

For my dear friends, who cared for Darrell as if you were caring for me. Your strength, prayers, and home-cooked meals comforted him when he was at his weakest.

To Sandy, there are no words on earth to describe the depths of our friendship.

My sweet, sweet in-laws, Joe and Barb— you have always been a rock for us.

And to the entire Saint Simons Island: it was utterly amazing to see, hear, and feel the community rise up and care for one of their own. I had heard stories about it, but to have been the recipient of it and to experience the power of like-minded hearts was riveting.

To Rebekah, thank you for sharing your God-gift and helping me make this book come to life.

Table of Contents

The Takedown

Walking into my office, I closed the door behind me and sat down at my desk. With a long exhale, my burning head fell forward into my hands.

What is happening to me? Oh my God, I can't…I'm not gonna make it.

My mind was in a thick fog, made worse by an all-over throbbing headache. I felt the sensation of black tar oozing all over my body, and there was nothing I could do to stop it.

Alright, pull it together, get it together.

It was a Wednesday in March of 2021, and I was in the middle of my morning clinic hours as a chiropractor and integrative nutritionist in Saint Simons Island, Georgia.

I loved the practice I had built, tucked into a corner in Redfern Village, on an island where long stretches of salty marsh are sometimes interrupted by manicured lines of royal palms. The cozy, coastal home I had built nearby, exactly two and half miles door to door from work, served as both a sanctuary and a home office.

The previous year had delivered explosive growth to my practice, both locally and internationally, with the COVID pandemic raging. 80% of my patients were virtual consults, but the other 20% were local and insisted on seeing me in person, like the one I had seen the previous Thursday. She told me her husband had COVID, even though she wasn't showing any symptoms.

My schedule was hectic, but people were desperate. Our phones and email inquiries were blowing up. Folks needed our help. Surely this would all be over soon. Surely I would stay healthy as usual. I needed to stay healthy. I was the one teaching life balance, sleep hygiene, and supplements.

What's happening to my body?

I thought back two weeks prior when I had started with some nasal congestion and sinus pressure, which was abnormal for me. It felt like I was in a fishbowl, and I would try to blow my nose and nothing was there.

It was early springtime in Georgia, so I chalked it up to allergies, increased my supportive supplements—Vitamin C, D, Zinc, and Quercetin—and confirmed my suspicion by taking an over-the-counter antihistamine, which helped.

But there was that weird cough.

It started Saturday when I was out playing golf. I told my friends, "Oh, it must be something blowing in the air." It was a dry cough, but it persisted through the week. Now my chest was beginning to feel heavy and tight.

I don't know what to do right now. I can't even think, I can't even think. I have to go home.

My assistant was outside in the hallway. I usually pop my head out for the next patient, but I wasn't coming. She came into the office to check on me, and by the look on my face, she could tell something was off.

I have been in practice almost 30 years and I have never called in sick or not showed up.

"I have to go," I told her. "I need you to cancel everybody."

Grabbing my laptop and my purse, I walked out. I don't even remember driving home.

Snow in My Lungs

I wasn't feeling well, but being in my own space and not having to be with patients helped me to rein in my huge concern. I called my friend, Sandy, who suggested I call Dr. Erwin immediately. Dr. Erwin, a colleague, friend, and our concierge MD on the island, came over later that day and gave me a COVID test. I rested on the living room couch the remainder of the evening, surrounded by my fur babies, my two Boston terriers, Braccio and Gianna, and my bull terrier, Cara Mia.

Dogs have a way of knowing when something isn't right. They all stayed close to me, keeping vigil while I tried telling myself this was a cold virus that would pass quickly.

The next morning, I woke up with a fever, worsening congestion, and a metallic taste in my mouth. The dogs were whining to go outside, and I dragged myself up to let them out. I sat on the couch, dazed, taking inventory of my symptoms, when my phone rang.

"Hey, Sage, it's Michael."

"Hi Michael, I wasn't expecting to hear back from you so soon."

"Yeah, well, we got your test results back. You're positive for COVID."

I froze. I felt a sinking sensation in my chest and sat there, holding my breath, not knowing what to say or do.

"Are you there, Sage?"

"…Yes, I'm here. What do I do now?"

"Well, you know the drill. Lots of fluids, rest, and let me know if you start having any trouble breathing. How are you feeling now?"

"Um, I'm okay. I have a little bit of a fever."

"Alright, well, I'll run by and give you a steroid shot just to keep things under control."

"Ok…ok, thanks."

"Is Darrell coming in this weekend?"

"Yes…he'll be here tomorrow."

"Ok, good, let him take care of things at home. Tell him he can call or text any time if he has any questions."

"Ok, Michael. Thank you."

I hung up and sat there, stunned. The things I should have done—taking my supplements, drinking more water, calling my colleagues for treatments—all went out the window. I needed someone to take over. I couldn't think straight. I looked down at my phone…

Thursday, March 4th — *The day I found out I had COVID.* Lying down on the living room couch, I pulled my favorite soft, blue fleece blanket over my body, covering myself up to my neck. I was afraid. I had seen this fear in the eyes of my patients. I knew too much about what this virus was capable of…I had been following the numbers. Almost 150 people had already died in Glynn County alone from COVID.

I reached over to the coffee table and grabbed my Bible, opened it, and let it rest on my chest for comfort. Closing my eyes, I began to pray, asking God to help me, to strengthen me for whatever was coming. As I prayed, I drifted off…

"Honey, gather some belongings. I'm taking you to the ER."

It was the deep, familiar voice of my husband, Darrell, as he stood over me with Dr. Erwin behind him. My memory was foggy from the high fever, and my eyes were sore and burning as I opened them to focus. My long, black hair was barely held together by the hair tie I put in two days ago. Large strands were pasted to the side of my face from hours of tossing back and forth on the couch.

I remembered coming home from work six days prior and calling my friend Sandy, who urged me to call Dr. Erwin, to have a COVID test. Sandy had been checking in with me over the weekend. My fever had been up and down over that time.

It was Tuesday morning, and as Dr. Erwin was going about his usual routine—taking the kids to school, then heading home to grab a second cup of coffee and look over his schedule, something unusual happened. He heard a voice say,

"Turn the car around and go check on Sage."

The message was so strong that he turned his car around, showed up at our door, knocked briefly, and walked in on his own. He walked straight over to the couch. As soon as he looked at me, he said,

"Darrell, take her to the ER now!"

Darrell stopped what he was doing, and immediately walked over to me, nudging me gently on the shoulder, "Sage, come on, honey, we have to go."

"Okay. Okay," I mumbled, pulling myself up obediently to pack a bag. I was delirious with a high fever; my breathing was labored. Yet I found the resources to begin gathering things I needed, things I always needed…my electric toothbrush, floss, vitamins, my computer, and patient files. I was on autopilot and packed as if I was going to the Hilton on a weekend vacation.

Darrell is not one to panic, but he had been home with me since Friday, arriving by Uber since he knew I wasn't feeling well enough to pick him up as usual. Darrell works remotely in our hometown of Milwaukee. Every six weeks, he visits for two to three weeks.

Our arrangement was financially motivated. We wanted to be together, but Darrell was riding out his 30-year career as a mechanic with UPS to get his pension. I understood how important that was for him. Darrell understood how important warmth and sunshine were for me.

After we married in 2007, I tried living in Milwaukee, but it was a disaster for my health, both physically and mentally. I ended up building a house and a thriving integrative medicine practice in Saint Simons beginning in 2015. Although the arrangement could be stressful at times, knowing it was temporary helped us endure the long periods of separation. We talked on the phone constantly, Darrell being the more talkative of the two of us. We both looked forward to his upcoming retirement when we could live together in Saint Simons permanently.

Darrell arrived on Friday, just one day after my COVID diagnosis. When his crystal blue eyes met mine, my steely resolve that I would rebound, began to wane when I saw the fear in his face.

"Do you need anything?" he asked, trying to sound normal, but his deer-in-the-headlights stare gave him away.

"Just some water, please."

I tried to sit up on the couch, but quickly slumped back down. My fever had begun to climb over 100 degrees up to 102, which in my mind was still manageable.

I'm in good hands. I'm gonna be ok.

Darrell likes to say I have a higher pain threshold than anyone he knows. He's used to me being strong and taking care of things—my patients, the house, the bills, our dogs.

It's true, I am independent and capable. I rarely ask for help, because I'm usually the one offering it. It's not a pride thing, I've just been given a lot of internal strength. Although I'm introverted, I enjoy helping others.

Darrell and I knew we would be quarantining that weekend to keep him safe. Still, I was relieved he was home, because I knew at my gut level that this virus was pulling me down quickly. It was like I had been buckled onto a roller coaster, and like it or not, I was taking this ride.

"I talked to Dr. Erwin on the way home from the airport," Darrell said. "He says if you're not feeling better this weekend, he'll come by and do a vitamin drip on Sunday morning."

"Oh…ok."

Thank God for Michael…the vitamins will help me fight this off.

I had already been taking several herbs given to me by my colleague, Mark Brinson, an acupuncturist and master herbalist, who shares an office space with me. There were these three little vials, and I had to take six tiny tabs inside them, three times a day.

Friday night passed and Saturday too, and I was holding my own. I stared at the TV, not really watching. In and out of sleep, the dogs kept me company on the couch. I tried to let my body fight without the help of any fever-reducing medications.

Fever is a good sign that the body is waging war against invading viruses and bacteria by killing the sugar they feed on. I knew from my medical training that it was best, if possible, to let the fever run its course so that the body heat destroys all the sugar in your body, essentially starving the pathogen of its food source. A fever up to 102 is ok, but anything beyond that can be very dangerous.

On Sunday morning, my fever was still bouncing between 100 and 102. My thoughts teetered between *I got this, I'm good,* and when my fever would climb, *what in the world is going on? Why is it spiking again?*

Dr. Erwin came by and hooked up a vitamin drip. I felt better immediately, and thought I was moving into the clear.

By Sunday night, my fever shot up to 105. I became delirious. Darrell began checking my temperature obsessively and was becoming more panicked.

"We need to call somebody…I need to call Michael."

In and out of consciousness, feeling disconnected from my own body, I prayed in between fits of sleep. The only point of connection I felt was the grounding weight of my Bible on my chest.

Help me, God…help me.

As I lay there, my lungs were heavy, my head throbbing. Somewhere in the fog, a memory drifted into my consciousness… that night in 1999 when my boss, a wealthy doctor in Tampa, invited me to the Buccaneer stadium for an event, not telling me what it was...

For two years, I had been in Tampa and was a nanny at the time, in the process of getting my license to be a chiropractor. I tried to collect the kids to go with us, but they didn't want to go. He took me anyway–to a Billy Graham crusade.

It was the night I became a Christian.

When we walked into the stadium through one of the tunnels, I noticed the lights were dim. Hundreds of people filled the stands and a large group of listeners stood quietly listening on the field. At the front stood a large man, who I later found out was Billy Graham. Something made me stop and listen very intently.

Billy Graham was speaking about the Trinity, how God the Father, God the Son, and God the Holy Spirit are all One. I remembered growing up and being taught they were all separate, but when I heard Billy Graham say it, I knew it was true. My face lit up, and it was as if my spirit cried out, "Yes! I get that! That's what I want!"

My boss was intrigued by my reaction. Grabbing my hand, he said,

"Come on, let's go down there."

I walked with him down the bleacher steps to the field, through the crowd, until we were in the front row. Looking up at Mr. Graham, I fell to my knees where he prayed over me and I gave my heart to Jesus. It felt like every cell in my body was alive and energized; I was forever changed.

Growing up in an Italian Catholic family, I went to mass every single Sunday with my grandmother. My mother's family were Sicilian immigrants who came to the U.S. in the 1960s. Mom and I lived with my grandparents in Milwaukee after my parents divorced. I was only two years old.

Mom was often too tired to go to mass—she was a hairstylist who ran her own business—but she would drop Nanna and I off at church. Nanna was steady, dependable, and domestic: she taught me to garden, and sew, and do laundry. Papa, my grandfather, was the silent, six-foot-two, beautiful man of few words whose lap you could always crawl on for a sip of his beer.

While Mom and Papa stayed home on Sundays, Nanna and I went to mass like clockwork. As an adult, I tried to reconnect with the Catholic Church, but it felt so monotone to me…it didn't reach out and grab my heart.

During my first year of practice, I was introduced to a community church, which I liked. I didn't really understand much of what was said about a personal relationship with Jesus, but after my experience at Buccaneer Stadium, I began to put the pieces together. I understood what it meant to be born again and that it wasn't just about rules, regulations, and prayers.

My faith took root as I began to study the Bible. I took classes about spiritual gifts and boundaries. Then I dove into it head-on, surrounding myself with like-minded people who didn't just talk about their faith but actually lived it out.

Jesus, help me.

It was Tuesday morning at 9 a.m., and we were arriving at the ER at the Brunswick Campus of Southeast Georgia Health System. I was gasping for air.

This isn't good.

My breathing had been going downhill since 2:30 a.m. on Monday morning. I was told that Dr. Erwin gave me a steroid shot on Tuesday at 8 a.m. when he arrived, but I have no memory of it.

I couldn't think or react. But somewhere deep beyond my physical body, my spirit was praying. I thought about my many years of walking out the faith that had become so foundational to my daily existence. I knew the power of prayer, of a simple, childlike cry to God from a hurting soul or a broken body.

Lab tests and x-rays were ordered without much waiting. When the ER doctor came in with my X-ray results, he seemed almost angry with me. I guess he knew I was in the medical field. He waved the films in my face and asked me in an abrasive, patronizing tone,

"Do you *see* these films?"

He held my lung x-rays up to the light, and it was hard to believe they were mine. They were white as snow.

"Do you know what this means?"

I had a feeling they were a first-class ticket to the ICU.

"Yes, it's bad," was all I could manage. Even in my weakened state, I had enough sense to know I was very sick…*and* this guy was being a jerk.

"Your oxygen is at 40% and anything below 90% should be treated. We need to admit you right now."

He sighed deeply, as if I was inconveniencing him by being ill.

The nurses came in and moved me to a wheelchair. The next thing I knew, I was being whisked away to Intensive Care. What I didn't know was that after I was gone, the doctor told Darrell I had a 20% chance of survival.

My last memories before going into a medically-induced coma included two things: a pulmonologist putting a PICC line into my neck and a nurse washing my hair. There were several IVs put into my arm as well, but I have no recollection of that.

The pulmonologist was talking to me, while inserting a thick tube into the side of my throat, about an experimental procedure where they were going to extract my blood, spin it, clean it, and then put it back. He wanted to run a test to see if my kidneys could handle it. The procedure was painful and it felt like a fishing line was being placed through my neck, even worse than an IV in the arm.

My hair was down to the middle of my back, at the time. Once the pulmonologist was done, the nurse checked on me.

"I'd like to wash your hair…would that be ok?"

"Yes," I said. The nurse put my hospital bed all the way down so it was flat. I felt fuzzy in my head. (Later, I found out it was the drugs they gave me to relax.) She brought a plastic tub over to my bed, placing it under my head.

The nurse was gentle and comforting, making sure the water temperature was okay, massaging my scalp, and then gathering my thick, curly black hair up into a pile on top of my head and putting it all into a ponytail.

It may have been protocol for patients going into ICU, but it felt like she was doing it purely as an act of kindness.

I was not in control anymore. The hospital staff was now in charge, and I was at their mercy. I had no idea, but I was about to spend the next eight days fighting for my life.

One Foot in Heaven
One on Earth

Walking briskly down what seemed like a long corridor, I couldn't see where it ended. I was walking with purpose, like I knew where I was going. It wasn't a rushed feeling, like I might have in the Atlanta airport when I'm pressed for time and trying to make it to the gate. It was a happy, determined walk, as if I was walking to meet my closest friend I hadn't seen in a while.

I was excited. I felt energized, liberated, and completely free from any worries or cares. Surrounding me on every side was bright white light; the walls were made of sheer, white curtains, and the floor and ceiling were also white. The air surrounding me carried a natural perfume, like a garden in early summer when the roses are in full bloom, the temperature reminiscent of a perfect beach day—warm and comforting.

My trot was a combination of a fast military walk, heel strike, and arms at ninety degrees to gain better momentum. I picked up my pace, walking even faster. When suddenly, I was elated! I believed I knew where I was going—*home.*

I was abruptly halted by four people.

They appeared right in front of me, and I stopped. They were all beautiful and peaceful, their faces soft and loving, smiling warmly at me. I was shocked by their appearances, not knowing what to think…I wasn't expecting to see any of them.

The first person on the left was a bearded man in a brown robe; his skin was clean and smooth, without any blemishes, and his eyes were bright and kind. I recognized Him instantly as Jesus.

As my eyes took in each one, I saw Papa standing next to Jesus, then

Nanna right next to him, both looking exactly as I remembered them as a child. The last person I recognized was Mom, who stood slightly behind Nanna.

I don't know how long I stood there, taking in their presence and feeling surprised and overwhelmed, too much so to run up and hug them. None of them spoke at first, except for Jesus, who extended a warm hand to me and said, "I gave you a gift, to live your purpose. Now go, and do not fall into distraction."

His words were direct, but said with such love and compassion that I felt no offense, only acknowledgement and understanding. Standing there in His presence, I felt completely known without any sense of insecurity or self-consciousness.

Even though His words were few, the depth of meaning behind them sank deeply into my being. I immediately understood that He had given me the gift of healing, the gift of helping people, relieving their suffering by getting to the root causes of their illnesses. It wasn't only about my education and experience; it was God using me to bring wholeness to people He loves.

I also knew why He mentioned distractions. I thought about my career, and it was true— I was forever trying to do it all in my business—the patient care, social media, finances, marketing—I wasn't good at delegating, and it made me spin out and lose focus. I worried about money, about making sure I had enough patients. Many concerns pulled me away from exercising my primary gift of healing.

When I was with my patients, I would engage fully and be present with them, but as soon as they left, I would be scattered in ten different directions. It was affecting my own health and also my peace of mind.

Nanna also spoke to me, and what she said touched a deeply wounded part of my soul. I was raised by my mother, who was a career woman, and my grandmother, who was domestic. My mother always told me I could do anything I wanted to do; the sky was the limit. She raised me to follow my dreams and pursue my passions. Nanna, on the other hand, was gentle yet stern and taught me how to garden, cook, bake, clean house, make a bed properly, sew, do laundry, and nurture a family.

Somehow I thought as a woman I could do both exceptionally well. When it finally came time to have kids, I was physically unable. I was in my late thirties and moved to Milwaukee after Darrell and I married, thinking we would live near our extended family and raise our kids with their cousins, cheering at Little League games together. After several failed attempts at conceiving, I was beyond discouraged. Fertility treatments worked, but then I miscarried. We hired a surrogate, and she backed out.

I was angry at myself for waiting so long. The emptiness and heartache of my unmet desires caused me to battle depression, made worse by the long, cold Wisconsin winters. Darrell and I moved forward in our marriage, and I had found a place to thrive in Saint Simons, but the pain lingered in my heart over not having had the opportunity to raise children of my own.

Nanna spoke:

"Children cannot be raised by a parent who works. You have to pick either the children or the career. The woman can't have both."

What might sound like a judgment toward working moms felt like a blessing from Nanna; it ushered in a much-needed flood of forgiveness. I wanted both. I desired it with all my heart. I was grief-stricken that Darrell and I never had children, but I had enjoyed an amazing career. I witnessed first-hand what Nanna was talking about. The working moms I saw in my office often battled stress and anxiety over the tension between home and work.

Many felt like they came home from a full day of work only to clock in for their second shift. They would say they felt like a failure as a mom, and a failure as a career woman. I found myself encouraging them to give themselves permission for a season to be home with their young children, even when it was expensive or inconvenient.

Even though Nanna's opinion isn't a popular one by modern standards, my heart desperately needed to hear her say it was okay. It was okay that I had focused my life on helping and healing others. My grandmother, who was the primary domestic figure during my formative years, was telling me that I had done a great job, my career had been blessed. However, if I had tried to raise children, and also have a career, my affections would have been split. For me, it would have been a constant battle.

After Nanna spoke, I never did walk back through the corridor. I awoke abruptly, and I saw there were five hospital staff around me as they pulled the tube out of my throat.

Twilight Sleep

I woke up in a sea of chaos. The hospital staff was trying to extubate me, but I wasn't doing well. Coming back into my body, after being in the hallway of heaven, filled me with a crushing sense of loss. I had been separated from the ones who loved me most, and I wanted to go back. I wanted to be with them, bathed in light and happiness, and the feeling of true peace and being completely loved. My heart ached with the realization that I was back here, in this place, in this hospital, fighting for my life.

My body was unrecognizable to me. I felt broken. The sensation of my fragile frame against the mattress brought a heaviness to my heart as I realized how sick I had become.

I was groggy, still struggling to breathe, and the medical staff was flipping me on my stomach, sternly saying, "Turn, turn over, breathe, breathe." In my head I thought, *I am*, but no words came out.

My throat was burning and raw. I had no ability to direct energy toward any part of my body. I do not remember how long I was off the ventilator, but I do remember the moment they realized they had removed the ventilator prematurely.

"Do…not…put…me…under…again."

Somehow I managed to get these words out of my mouth at a volume the medical staff could hear and understand. My throat was swollen and painful, the thirst I felt was extreme, as if I had been left in a desert to die. But I found a way to let them know I had no intention of going back into a coma. [Darrell told me later that they called him and said, "The tube must go back in because she is not breathing on her own yet." When they told him I said, *"Do not put me under,"* he said, "You better listen to her!" That was the moment Darrell felt a glimmer of hope that his *fighting Sicilian* was coming back.]

The next thing I knew, they were shoving that godawful tube down my throat again. It's hard to describe the feeling of having a machine breathe for you. When they push the tube down your airway, it feels like your throat is being punctured. You might be ready to take a breath, but the machine isn't, and that feeling makes you panic.

As they slide the tube down, the anesthesiologist talks in a fake-comforting voice, telling you that you won't feel anything.

I felt it all.

Then everything went dark again. Down I went again, sinking back underneath a weighted blanket of sedation. They did not put me all the way under; I was placed in a twilight sleep.

Tuesday, March 16th

The ventilator stayed in for two more days. When I woke up, I was extremely clear and cognizant. Two nurses were on either side of me, pulling and guiding my body forward, talking me through removing the ventilator while gently pulling the tape off my face.

"Ok, we're going to pull this tube out and you might feel a little sting…"

Oh God, my throat.

It stung like multiple coordinated stabs as they pulled the ventilator tubing out. I felt lightheaded, as they pulled my body forward, and weak. So, so weak.

Once they put me back down on the bed, one of the nurses asked me, "Are you ok?"

I have no idea. I guess I'm alive. That's a start.

"Mmhm," I answered, feeling the fiery sting of my throat upon using my vocal cords.

"Can I get you some water?" the nurse asked, putting her face right up into mine to gauge my response.

I nodded, and my head fell sideways, limp from exhaustion. I couldn't use my voice again. Not yet.

The nurses walked out and I began assessing my body and my surroundings. I had tubes everywhere: a heart monitor, blood pressure monitor, and oxygen. I had a urine catheter, and there were three bags of medicines going into my IV. I felt shackled by all my attachments, barely able to move my body in any direction.

Coming out of twilight sleep is a gradual process. The medication they gave me made me very listless, groggy, and fuzzy. Yet I have specks of moments that flash in my mind.

I first remember being in a room with a slanted ceiling. I thought I was at home in my hospital bed in the living room and the slanted ceiling was my own stairwell. I assumed in my mind that Darrell wanted me to be comfortable, so he created a hospital setting in our home.

I did hear a great deal of noise – hammering, drilling, and sawing. I thought this was part of Darrell trying to makeshift this space in our home. All thoughts led to me being in my home.

The nurse brought me water in one of those large plastic cups with a handle and the fat straw. She would hold the straw to my mouth to help me drink. Every swallow of cold water was both relieving and harsh to my parched throat.

She wanted to position my cell phone so I could FaceTime with Darrell. This was the first time I saw myself…and boy, did I look rough. I could barely focus and I could not speak—my throat was too raw. Darrell's face appeared in the lower right corner of my screen, and the nurse spoke to him first.

"Hi, Darrell, I'm Sage's nurse, and just so you know, her throat is pretty sore, so she might not be able to talk much yet…"

"Ok, thank you," Darrell replied, his voice a mix of impatience and worry.

"Hi, honey, I know you can't talk, but…I'm so happy to see your face!"

I could tell he was getting emotional. His voice was shaky, but I was too dazed and drugged to empathize.

"Everything is good here. I'm taking care of our pets, our home…we all miss you…don't worry about a thing…you're gonna get better."

I tried to focus on his face, gave him a smirk and a thumbs up sign. That was all I could manage. Even that was exhausting. I was in and out of sleep that entire first day, feeling miserable.

Wednesday, March 17th

"What day is it?" I was starting to sound hoarse, but at least there was a little bit of my voice coming back.

"Well, let's see…It's very early on Wednesday, March 17th," the nurse replied, in a cheery voice. It was after midnight, and I couldn't sleep. I was still groggy, but it felt like my mind was working overtime to clear a path through the fog of anesthesia.

March 17th. I remembered that it was Friday the 5th when Darrell came home, and…three or four days later when he brought me to the ER. So…I've been here for…nine days?

"I've been here for nine days?"

"Yes, ma'am, that sounds about right," said the nurse, a middle-aged lady with a pleasant Georgia twang, long, straight bleached blonde hair and a sturdy frame.

"What drugs are they giving me?" I was still too tired for pleasantries and only wanted the information.

"Oh…well, let's see. There's, um, heavy-duty antibiotics…" She reached over and turned the bags to make sure she was reporting correctly.

"There's steroids for the inflammation, Heparin to keep your blood thinned out so you don't get any blood clots in your lungs, and Diflucan."

Wow. So many drugs.

My brain started rummaging through the file cabinet on pharmacology. I knew the Diflucan was for yeast, which was probably created by the IV that has heavy sugars and corn syrup in it. I also had a sense my gut was being compromised from all the medications.

I wanted to get out of there and go home. From the moment I opened my eyes, I wanted to go home. I missed my husband, my bed, and my dogs.

My dogs! They must be so upset.

In my mind's eye, I could see their pitiful faces…Cara Mia, my 50-pound Staffordshire Bull Terrier, who was 15 years old and my constant sidekick; 13-year-old Braccio, a mid-sized Boston Terrier who was the typical middle child, always vying for attention, and the puppy, Gianna, another Boston Terrier who was my 2-year-old toddler—all play and no patience. They were my babies, and I wondered if they were okay, if Darrell had been taking care of them.

Fear washed over me; I was scared! I had never been through anything like this before in my life and had no idea when they would release me. The negative thoughts began to overwhelm me, as I lay there in bed unable to sleep.

What if I don't get better? What if I have to be put under again? How long am I going to be a prisoner in this bed?

The only thing I could do was make up my mind that I was going to push and keep trying.

This is not a setback, this is a set-up. God has something bigger for me that I cannot even imagine.

I repeated this phrase many times to myself.

Fluids were essential, so I began to drink as much water as I could: ice water, room temperature, even water with a splash of cranberry, but that started a coughing fit. I was still coughing like I was when I was admitted, but this time, it was clear mucus.

The bouts of heavy coughing were exhausting. I was frustrated, because every time the vent from the AC above me kicked on, I would start hacking. It was a deep, ugly cough, the kind where you feel a panicked sense of drowning, struggling to catch your breath in between.

Trying to speak or exerting myself in any way would start the coughing. I wanted to suppress it, because I was already conjuring up a plan to go home and didn't want anything to deter me. The problem was the inflammation in my upper lung, caused by double pneumonia. (I never had lung issues in my life before COVID.)

The doctors made it very clear from the moment I stepped into the ER that to get released from the hospital, they needed a clear, clot-free CT scan of my lungs. The CT scan requires contrast, which is a dye that causes a drastic increase of gadolinium. Gadolinium is a metal that I knew was linked to dementia and other brain dysfunctions, and I chose to forgo the contrast, which stirred up problems between the staff.

At around 8 a.m., my nurse came in to let me know it was time for the scan, and she was working on prepping for my transport to have the test done. The nurse stepped out of the room; my curtain was drawn, so I could not see outside my room. My door was glass, and there were two side windows, long and narrow, framing the door. The curtain could pull in a half circle around my bed blocking my view outside the door, but I could hear everything.

My nurse was speaking with a male doctor, possibly the doctor in charge of the ward. Their conversation started friendly and began to escalate quickly. They were talking about me, and from what I heard, the nurse was supporting my decision to not take the contrast. The hospital was denying me the CT scan, and she was fighting for me to have one. They began arguing loudly. He was standing his ground and yet I heard him say,

"We'll figure this out."

And then there was silence. Deafening silence. All I could do was lay there and wonder what was going on, when finally another nurse walked in.

"What happened to the other nurse?" I asked.

"She went home. She needed to take a personal day."

"But what about my CT scan?"

She answered abruptly, "I am taking over, and I will help you get ready for your CT scan. I will have transportation arranged, and you will stay in your bed the whole time. Do you need anything right now?"

"No, thank you," I said, slumping back down into my bed.

This process took at least two hours to complete. Everything runs slower on "hospital time."

The nurse disconnected all my cords and tubes, which took several minutes with the plethora of my attachments. She and a transportation gentleman pushed me in my bed down the corridor to the elevator and away we went. Down in the elevator, down another corridor into a lobby-like room.

The nurse said, "I'll be right back. I will check us in."

At the same time, the transportation guy nodded his head, signaling his work was done, and he left. I waited in that bed with anticipation. I was told from the day I arrived, a clear CT was my ticket out. I was anxious. The nurse whisked around the corner and looked at me and said,

"Ready? Here we go!"

The machine was set up, and there I was, waiting for my instructions as everyone scurried behind a wall.

"You will feel like you are peeing your bed, not to worry, it is the IV," said the nurse.

"Ok," I said.

This is a terrible feeling and a really miserable position to be in. Is this what my patients have to go through when prescribed a CT?

Before I was wheeled out, I heard the nurse say, "Run that, STAT!"

Oh good, yes, run it STAT! I want to know when I will get out of here.

Time went very slowly that morning. Darrell and I Face-Timed four times that day; seeing his face made me all the more determined to get home. I checked with the nurse every hour on my results.

Finally, around 1:30 p.m., the nurse walked in with a big smile,

"Your results are in. CT is clear."

I slumped back in my bed, I was so relieved, and yet, I had worked myself into pure exhaustion. I was tired.

My battles weren't over yet. I had not slept in two days since I had been taken off the ventilator, and I was pretty sure it was the Heparin. I could feel that it was too strong for my body; my heart was racing, and I could not calm it down. I asked the nurse if we could stop the Heparin, since I had been given 1 ½ bags already. She obliged, but the wrath followed when the lung specialist visited my room later that afternoon.

All of the tubes coming from my body exited down the left side, so the nurses and doctors would come around the foot of my bed to attend to me on the left.

However, shortly before lunchtime, the lung doctor walked into my room and threw back the curtains in front of my bed. He stood on my right side, forcing me to turn my body over, along with all of my connections, to see his face. It was uncomfortable and awkward, and I think he knew it.

The doctor was of average height, with a full head of wavy, salt and pepper hair that was disheveled, and very distinct, masculine facial features.

Standing over me with his arms folded on his chest and a stern disapproval on his face, he asked,

"Who do you think you are? Why are you not taking the Heparin?"

Before I could answer, he launched into a lecture.

"Don't you know I have 26 years experience as head of the pulmonary department? It is critical that you stay on protocol and take the Heparin…"

Who do I think I am? Who does he think he is?

Even in my weakened state, I was not one to take this kind of verbal beating. As I listened to his rant, the Italian in me wanted to jump up and dish it right back to him. It wasn't my usual response, but for some reason, I took a different tact. When there was a pause, I interjected,

"With all due respect, sir, I appreciate your position, but the CT scan results came back and all was clear."

His face went pale, and I knew then that he had not read the results before entering my room. It caught him off guard, yet he quickly regrouped and sternly stated again that I needed to take the Heparin prophylactically—for prevention. He would not leave without an answer on whether or not I would take it.

"Can I think about it?"

He huffed. "Fine."

The doctor whisked out of the room, right after warning me that if I did not comply, he would take himself off my case.

He did just that.

This was an educated decision that I did not take lightly. I had discussed it with my hematologist, Dr. Moran, and he agreed with me that we had bigger issues to manage. Taking another chemical might create new problems.

Dr. Moran and I had a long history. I was no newbie when it came to dealing with doctors and traditional medical treatment, which often included medications with dangerous side effects.

In 2011, I was diagnosed with LGLL, Large Granular Lymphocytic Leukemia, an extremely rare blood disorder that affects the white blood cells called lymphocytes. LGLL is more of a chronic health condition than the aggressive cancer normally associated with the word *leukemia*. It is not considered to be a genetic condition, but the jury is still out on what exactly causes it. In my opinion, it is most likely the perfect storm of oxidative stress, environmental toxins, and nutrient deficiencies. LGLL has co-conditions, and my co-condition just happens to be severe anemia.

My immune system had taken a major hit, and doctors tried me on several different medications considered "standard therapy" for my condition that made me feel terrible and didn't improve my bloodwork. Over time, with the support of Dr. Moran, I discovered I could manage my condition by listening carefully to my body, and by using diet, exercise, and supplements to support my immune system.

Because LGLL affects white blood cell production, it's co-condition can be hemolytic anemia. For four years, I have needed blood transfusions every seven weeks. Aside from that, I took no medications for my condition besides Desferol, which helps to chelate the iron in your blood after a transfusion. (You can read more about this in my book, *Thrive with LGL-Leukemia and Autoimmune; Not Just Survive.*)

A couple of hours after my encounter with the offended lung specialist, a medic came into my room and asked if I remembered him. I did not. He said he was in the ER when I arrived and that my lungs were full of white "clouds" all over the X-ray because of the cytokine reaction to my lungs with COVID. He asked me directly,

"Why won't you take the Heparin?"

He heard that I was resisting. The medic was much nicer than the lung doctor. I thanked him for visiting, but I had made up my mind—I was not taking the Heparin preventatively. Once he realized he wasn't going to convince me, the conversation was over. He left my room.

All day long the nurse came in to deliver the water I requested, assisting me like a young child with a straw. As the day dragged into evening, the nurse changed her approach. She dropped an unopened bottle of water on my tray table and walked out.

Wow, ok, I guess I'm on my own here. No big deal. I can do this.

I picked up the mini Pure Life water bottle and tried turning the cap. It wouldn't budge. I tried again and again, twisting with all my might, using different grips, but the cap wouldn't budge.

I can't even open a water bottle? Oh my God. I'm gonna need help. What else can I not do by myself? Am I helpless? A person who has always considered themselves helpful?

I had to decide at that moment if I was going to be a victim or not.

I chose to fight.

It was me and that stupid bottle of water, and we were going to the mat.

Fifteen minutes later, I finally got it open. Exhausted, I rewarded myself with a long swig of water.

Waking Up Wired

Thursday, March 18th

The ICU ward was full and just about every room was occupied. Within hours, the rooms became empty. One gentleman next to me moaned incessantly that entire day and into the next, and then it was quiet.

The atmosphere in ICU was intense and stressful; you could sense the tension in the air, even though the nurses did a good job trying to hide it.

I faintly wondered why the rooms around me were emptied so quickly. I figured it out when two nurses came into my room very early on Thursday morning with serious looks on their faces.

"Is everything ok?"

The nurses looked at each other, and one nurse spoke.

"We've been talking, and we don't understand why you are so…" She paused and chose her words carefully…"strong? I mean, people do not leave from here…from ICU…I mean, they are not going home!"

I looked at the nurses in shock, realizing for the first time what they were saying and why the rooms around me emptied out so quickly. The moaning from that man stopped when he died. People were dying all around me. A wave of terror washed over me, and my eyes filled with tears.

"Please pray for me," I said. "God has a plan for me. I have nothing to do but lie here and heal and pray…I am at the mercy of our Lord. Pray that God gives me the strength to persevere through this."

The nurses looked at each other and asked if I needed anything before they left my room. Their heads were down, and it was the first time I had witnessed real emotion from the staff.

The nurses and doctors were in a war zone and losing battles daily, but when they would enter my ICU room, their chins were lifted, and they were friendly and bright-eyed. It was an inspiration to me, as I was dealing with my own defeating thoughts about getting well.

When my mind would begin to spin in negativity, I looked up at the ceiling in my room and said to God,

You have me!? Because I desperately need You now, every second of the day!

Coming out of a coma, everything was fuzzy and unclear. I had lost ten days of my life and sixteen pounds. Weak and exhausted, yet unable to sleep, I felt trapped in that hospital room connected to all their tubes and cords. My body ached. It was painful to talk, but I knew I needed my supplements, which were somewhere nearby. I whispered to the nurse,

"Where is my bag?"

"...And my computer?"

I was starting to put pieces together. I remembered I packed my patient files and computer.

"It's back there," she said, pointing to the far corner of the room.

"Your computer is there too," she assured me. I was frustrated, not being able to get up and grab my own things.

"Can I take my supplements?"

"No, you're not allowed."

The nurse left the room. I was thinking about pulling the tubes out that held me down but also knowing it would trigger the nurse to come right back and scold me. I was stuck. Nobody would give me my supplements, because they weren't in protocol.

I started feeling anxious, like I needed a rescue. I knew what hospitals were famous for, and it wasn't always for saving lives. It was part of the reason I practiced integrative medicine—to keep people out of places like this.

On the second night of lying in bed wide awake until the early morning hours, I was suffering with a sharp pain in my left shoulder.

I texted my colleague and asked if there was anything I could do to help make myself more comfortable. It was probably 4 a.m., and I prefaced my request with, "When you wake up…". He texted right back, and I was shocked he was awake so early. He responded with,

"Sage, it's good to hear from you. The best thing you can do is just rub it out, try to stay relaxed. I can't wait for you to get out of there so you can get rehabilitated. I can give you an acupuncture treatment."

Not what I wanted to hear. I needed relief now.

Mark Brinson is a well-known master herbalist and acupuncturist who brews his own pain-relieving topical called "Evil Bone Water." He shares an office space with me at Redfern Village. Together we make a great team.

Mark is about to have a regular day at work, and I'm stuck in here, hurting.

I texted another colleague, Dr. Tina, who I've known for 30 years and begged her to get me out of the hospital.

"I need an intervention. Can you come rescue me? Get me out of here!"

All I kept thinking about was the 1990 movie *Jacob's Ladder*, which put chiropractors on the map. In it, Danny Aiello plays the chiropractor whose patient is in the hospital with severe back pain. Aiello shows up, unannounced, scoops his patient up and carries him in his patient gown out of the hospital and brings him to his clinic, where he gives him a chiropractic adjustment.

In my mind, I was the patient who needed the intervention.

"You mean you're not enjoying your stay at the Ritz?" Tina quipped. "All I need are some scrubs and a getaway car, and I'll be right there."

I texted back, slow but steady.

"Seriously, this feels like prison. They won't even give me my vitamins because they aren't 'protocol'."

It felt good to vent to a like-minded friend who I knew would understand my dilemma.

"Well, that's not surprising," Tina texted back. "Hey, I have a feeling you'll be out soon. You're a fighter! We're all rooting for you, Sage."

No one will help. I'm stuck here.

I rubbed my shoulder, trying to divert my mind from the pain and the restlessness rising in my body, being harnessed to that uncomfortable bed.

While I was awake at night with the hours creeping by slowly, I felt my brain becoming clearer and firing strong. I used that time to check off all the things they told me I needed to do to consider being discharged. The nurse walked around my room with me at midnight. I brushed my teeth, which felt like a monumental task, but also made me feel independent and stronger. I had her move me from the chair to the bed and back to the chair. I prayed. I prayed hard.

This is not a setback, this is a set-up. God has a plan for you. Keep your eyes on Him.

In the mornings, the nurse came in and updated my marker board, stating the date and goals for that day. I liked this, because it was a way of grounding me in the present and focusing my mind on what needed to be done for me to make progress. (I didn't know this at the time, but Darrell called every morning and asked the nurse to do this.)

I spent time talking to every nurse that would come in, sharing pet photos and life in general. I wanted them to know I acknowledged and appreciated the effort they were putting into my care. I never hesitated to call the nurses when I needed them. I was instructed not to get up on my own, so I was at the mercy of how fast they came. They tended to my needs quickly, which helped calm my anxious thoughts.

I could hear the nurses' conversations outside my room. This was enough to occupy my interest; I didn't even want to watch TV.

A woman was yelling at another woman about her 80-year old mother, who had fallen out of bed. The daughter was angry at the staff for letting this happen. The argument went on for at least fifteen minutes or so, and I became uncomfortable.

I pushed my call button, which the nurses called a cowbell. I was hoping to help a nurse out of that situation by giving her a reason to check on me, but they sent a different nurse to answer my request. The yelling continued for ten more minutes, and then, it stopped. I assumed the woman stormed out.

My nurse came into my room and did not display any emotion from the altercation, so I asked her,

"Are you ok? Everything alright?"

"All good," she said. "How are you feeling?"

She was genuine in her concern. I marveled at her, knowing not many people could pull this off, not carrying emotions from one situation into another. In my experience, it would usually seep out.

There were quite a few episodes that happened outside my door over the next couple of days. Once again, the nurses came into my room calm, cool, and collected. I was unable to watch TV with all the drama happening in real life; TV would have been too stimulating.

I was realizing the depth of my empathy. I knew I was compassionate, but in this instance, I was more worried about the hospital staff and the conflict and death around me than I was worried about my own healing.

You're here to heal, Sage. Breathe, relax. Let it go…they will work it out.

I had to talk to myself like this over and over again. I was facing my vulnerabilities in recovery. This was just the beginning.

My legs were weak, and I was unsure of holding my body upright. Coming out of a coma, it felt like my mind was asking me, *What do you want? Do you want to fight and live or not?*

Every time the question arose, I made a firm decision in my mind that I wanted to live, and I wanted to get better and go home.

But there were moments of fear and self-doubt. When my resolve would weaken, God would send me a sign to keep my head lifted. Like Vera.

Vera was a cleaning lady who came to the floor daily. Her pear-shaped body and determined gait reminded me of an African American version of Vicky on the Carol Burnett show. Vera was a heavy-set lady in her 60s with a short bob of kinky, curly hair with gray roots, as if she hadn't updated her color in a while.

She pushed around her circular rolling garbage can with all kinds of supplies hanging from it—sprays, wipes, garbage bags, and towels…lots of towels. The garbage can was parked in the middle of the hallway that seemed to be shaped like a cul-de-sac.

Vera knocked lightly on my door and asked to clean, and I was happy to see her. I felt so vulnerable, completely at the mercy of the hospital staff who would determine my fate. While I lay there I prayed,

God, send me a sign. Let me know I'm not alone here.

The wheels of Vera's cart would make a rhythmic, whirring sound as they rolled across the hospital floor. She carried herself with strength and purpose, moving through my room with clear intention and a sense of unwavering dignity. Vera seemed peaceful and happy, and something about her presence lifted my spirits.

She brought in her mop and would begin cleaning the floor while stopping every few minutes to wipe something with the rag that was on her hip. Vera was fussing about the young folks and how they don't clean as well as others, carrying on about it while she was cleaning and pushing the mop.

"Now, why don't they see this when they come in?" She stopped and asked me while leaning down to pick up a large piece of lint in the middle of the walkway.

"Yeah, you're right," I said, "that piece of fuzzy plastic has been sitting on the floor since the other day."

"Hmm. You know these young folks, they just clean 'round the edges."

She shook her head and then turned to look right at me… and it felt like she was looking into my soul.

"How you feelin', sweetie?"

"I'm getting better," I said, trying to convince myself as well as Vera.

"Good, because Jesus' got you!"

My heart leapt; she had caught me off guard.

"Thank you, I needed to hear that," I said, with tears in my eyes and a smile on my face.

I watched her go back to her rolling garbage can and linger. Her eyes were closed with her head bowed. I realized she was praying. Vera was not just the cleaning lady, she was a prayer warrior sent to pray over the patients whose rooms she cleaned.

For what seemed like hours, I watched her through the glass window of my room. After cleaning every room, she would go in and out of rooms, and then bow her head over her garbage can. No one questioned her or said anything to her. Everyone scurried around Vera and her cumbersome cart. But she was her own person with her own mission, and Vera carried it out faithfully, day after day in that hospital ward.

I took it as a sign from God that He had His people watching over me.

I'm gonna be fine, I told myself. *I'm gonna be fine.*

It was Thursday night, and I requested a small dose of Benadryl to sleep, knowing if I could get just half a dose, 12mg, it might make me drowsy enough to drift off. The doctor cleared my request and prescribed it. When the girl came in to administer it, before I could even turn to see what was happening, she shot a full dose into my IV.

"There's your Benadryl," she said, in a matter-of-fact tone.

"Ok, thank you. How much was it?"

She didn't answer, so I just lay there and took a deep breath. *Thank God. I hope this works.*

It was like speed. She gave me a full dose, and I had the opposite reaction.

Another night of total sleeplessness.

As I lay wide awake from the Benadryl, trying to relax, my door opened suddenly, and Dr. Moran, my primary doctor, appeared looking disheveled and flustered. He whisked in and put his hand at my foot, blurting out,

"Thank God you are here!"

He was out of breath.

"Yes, I am here…why…what happened?" I asked. I was trying to figure out what was going on with him.

"When I came to visit you…you were in a coma, and they had you next door. I walked in there tonight, and the room was neat…it was cleaned and sterile, and I thought maybe you had…"

"Oh my Lord, no! I am here, I am okay!"

Oh wow. He thought I had died.

"I realize that," he said, his breathing beginning to settle, "but it took an effort to get the information out of nurses to finally tell me where you were."

His brown eyes softened.

"I am glad to see you are okay," he said.

"I am glad you are here. Thank you for visiting me. I have to tell you something."

I couldn't wait to tell him my story about the pulmonologist. I was so afraid he would prevent me from getting discharged, and I confessed my concern to Dr. Moran.

"Don't worry about that guy, I went to school with him…I'll talk to him," he explained.

I was relieved, yet part of me was still worried about my plan to get out of there.

I was finished with all the IV meds and moving to the pills they ordered. I requested probiotics, because I knew the faster I could try to heal my gut, the better. They had it in the pharmacy, so I was given a probiotic twice a day. I was not allowed to take my vitamins.

They tried to put me on Pepcid AC, and I questioned them. I do not have a history of GERD or indigestion. I asked why I needed to take it, and no one had an answer except to say it was protocol. I declined the medication.

I was making progress quickly. The nurse removed more tubes, and now I could get up more easily with their help. The doctors of different specialties came to visit, as they were all involved in my care. They were shocked at how much progress I had made in a short period of time being off the ventilator.

A physical therapist came by to test my function and range of motion. An occupational therapist came by to see if I could feed myself. I had to eat applesauce while she watched and graded me.

The night nurse and I had long talks about post-COVID care, the hospital food, our pets, and how important it was for me to go home.

I asked her, "Isn't it true if I continue to stay here there is a chance of me getting re-infected with something else or even COVID again?"

The nurse was reluctant to answer, but she simply said, "Yes."

I was a bit calmer and relieved about my clear CT scan.

I was ready to go home.

Friday, March 19th

I was still in an ICU room, yet the doctor had explained to me the day before that they were short on beds. Even though my room was in the ICU, I was not technically an ICU patient. I explained to the nurse that if I continued to stay in the hospital eating their unhealthy food, there was a chance I could slide backwards. She agreed that getting me home would be the best thing for my recovery so I pleaded with her to help me convince the doctors I was ready to be discharged. But I did not realize her shift was ending.

That morning, the nurses changed shifts. I was sad to say goodbye to my PM nurse. Now I would need to convince the doctor in charge that I was capable of managing myself at home, since it was only day four of being out of the coma.

At home, I would have a full-time caregiver since Darrell was on leave from work, and colleague practitioners to help me heal, and my favorite nutritious foods along with all my supplements.

In the four nights since they had taken me off the ventilator, I had not eaten much or slept at all. I was restless and full of angst, and I couldn't shake it. I wanted to go home, and it felt like I was starting to crack emotionally. My PM nurse comforted and reassured me that the morning shift nurse, Joe, would be a great advocate for me.

About an hour later, Joe walked in and was all business, but he treated me with kindness.

He bustled around the room, checking my IV and making notes on a clipboard.

"I want you to know I'm aware of your wishes to go home. Unfortunately, I don't have the authority to release you, but I will help relay all of your progress to the doctors so they can make the best informed decision."

"Oh, thank you," I said, and felt the tension in my neck relax as I was convinced Joe was on my side.

"Sage, this place has nothing to offer you anymore. Your best bet is to get home. You know how to take better care of yourself. I know who you are and what you do!"

Joe proceeded to clear up the meds list in the computer, since I had stopped taking everything listed. He disconnected almost all my tubes, heart connector, blood pressure cuff, oxygen, etc.

"You don't need any of this anymore. We have a room on a lower level. You are being transferred to a regular room."

I looked at the door, and there was transportation with a wheelchair ready to go. This was all happening so fast; I was already impressed with Joe.

This guy's a mover and a shaker.

About the same time, the doctor in charge entered my room, moving swiftly as most of the doctors did, checking my stats and asking me how I was doing.

"I'm doing great," (probably overly enthusiastic) I said, looking over at Joe.

He took my cue, parroting my response.

"She is progressing rapidly, walking, eating, using the bathroom…she is doing very well."

I knew I had to get right to the point, or as fast as she walked in, she would leave to visit the next patient. If I didn't do it then, I would be stuck there over the weekend. On the weekends, nothing happened, and the staff was significantly smaller. I decided to be direct and asked the doctor,

"Can I get discharged today?"

She came right back with, "It is unusual to get discharged so soon after being taken off a ventilator. I'm not sure."

I knew I had to respond quickly. I had about one minute or less to convince her I needed to go home.

"I have been very compliant and finished all the meds they have prescribed. Please, I want to go home and sleep. I've been up for the last four days."

"Well, your potassium levels are low!" she said with intensity.

I could feel my blood pressure rise.

I come into this hospital practically on my deathbed, and now you are concerned about my potassium? What do you think I do for a living?

I kept these thoughts to myself and softly replied, "I have asked for a banana, but there are none."

Joe agreed with a head nod.

The doctor paused, lingering in thought for a few moments and said, as she began moving for the door, "I will order potassium pills and retest your labs. If the levels are good, then I will discharge you this afternoon."

"Great!" I said.

The doctor walked out to continue her rounds. I looked over at Joe again and said,

"You are my witness…let's get this done."

One Step Closer to Home

Joe was lean and about 6'2"; he loaded two of my bags on one shoulder and three bags on the other. The rest he loaded on transportation. He helped me out of bed, and before I knew it, we were off to my other room on a lower level, whizzing down the corridor together.

We arrived at my new room, which was much more cheerful and bright, with larger windows. I thanked Joe and said goodbye, and he was gone.

I was so excited to be in my new, bigger room because it was the next step to going home.

Oh God, please do not let me stay here long.

A young lady walked in who spoke with a syrupy southern accent.

"I'm here to get some vitals on you. Are you comfortable? Can I get you anything?"

"Yes," I replied, "Please, two big cups of ice and plenty of water."

I was on a mission. She took my vitals, and within a few minutes, left the room and came back with my ice and water.

"Here ya go. Is there anything else?"

"Thank you, that will work."

I closed my eyes, and a wave of extreme exhaustion and grogginess filled my head. I could still feel the after-effects of the anesthesia. I heard the hammering and drilling outside my room again. I drifted into the place in between sleep; I really thought it was Darrell and his dad working on projects around me so they could keep an eye out for me.

It's their way of getting closer to me since no one can visit me.

At one point, I swore I saw a Green Bay Packers Cheesehead on the crash cart.

I knew it, I knew my father-in-law and husband were around here. They left a clue.

Lying there trying to discern between reality and fantasy, a feeling of sadness continued to grow inside my heart. Tears welled up in my eyes as it hit me—I had not slept in four days.

Push through this, Sage. You made it this far..."

My attempt at positive self-talk was interrupted when a new nurse walked in.

"Hi, I am David, your nurse. Are you comfortable? Do you need anything?"

"No, thank you," I replied. "I'm all set."

But then I remembered I needed every advocate I could get.

"You have an accent, David. Where are you from?"

"I'm from New Jersey...I'm here today and gone tomorrow. I travel around to different hospitals and do fill-in work."

"Really?" I asked, genuinely interested.

"Hey, David, I do not plan on staying here, and I need your help. The doctor promised that if my potassium levels are adequate, I can go home today. I want to go home! I have help at home. I need sleep, and I've been here way too long. Can you please help me?" I pleaded.

"Yeah, sure," said David without hesitation. "Hell, I'm a traveling nurse...I don't mind speaking up to these doctors!"

"Great," I said with relief. "Thank you. I need the potassium pills first and then a blood draw.

"Ok," David said, "Let me go check on those orders."

A few minutes after he left, the aide came in asking if I would like a tray of food.

"Oh, no thank you. I do not plan on staying long," I said, with a big grin. I didn't know how long it would take to get pills and labs done, but I was thinking I could leave by 1 p.m.

David was on the ball, delivering me three very large potassium pills in a small cup. I thanked him and sat there, thinking about how huge those pills were and how raw my throat was; it was still so sore and inflamed. Just looking at the size of those pills made my throat hurt worse.

David seemed very busy, yet he was following through on our plan and I was grateful. I looked up at the clock and back down at the pills again. I couldn't help but wonder—did the doctor do this on purpose? Was this a test to see if I really was ready to go home?

One at a time with slow sips of water, I took each pill. It took me twenty minutes to get those three pills down. Then I realized ice-cold water probably wasn't the best choice to help the pills dissolve. I rubbed my belly, praying and pleading for them to dissolve. I was upset it took me so long to swallow them, but I buried the negative thoughts and sat there feeling happy, thinking about how I would be home soon.

An hour went by, and I was wondering about the blood draw when Darrell walked in. He seemed to appear out of nowhere like a magician…Ta-Daaa!

He was carrying two large duffel bags and had a huge smile on his face. The sight of him made me well up with emotion; I had not seen him for ten days. My husband landed in my arms, hugging me so tightly the tears dripped out of my eyes. I was overwhelmed with his tenderness and care. Lingering in my arms for a long time, I finally spoke first, "It's so good to finally be with you!"

We let go of our embrace, and it registered in my mind that he had brought two bags with him.

"Why did you bring the duffel bags?" I asked, concerned.

"I do not plan on staying. I want to go home!"

I was upset. My mind was so fixed on being discharged that day; I was not remotely open to any other plan, especially one that included staying in the hospital.

"I wasn't sure, so I packed things just in case," Darrell said. "I have juice for you, your essential oils, and some things to give you comfort. Look at this…"

He pulled out a large, colorful quilt with pretty pinks and greens, and opened it up for me to see.

"The ladies from church made it for you and prayed over it for you."

I was so touched, and yet I was overwhelmed by his energy and enthusiasm.

"Honey, thank you so much for all these wonderful things, but we need to focus!" I was not about to allow my resolve to weaken.

"Why?" Darrell asked, confused.

"Because I need to get out of here, and I am waiting for the lab lady to draw my blood to check my potassium levels. The doctor promised if they were good she would sign my discharge papers today," I said, emphatically.

"Oh ok, well I can go find the nurse. What's her name?"

"*His* name is David."

With that, Darrell took off down the corridor looking for him.

After Darrell left, his phone rang, and it was a FaceTime request from our pastor.

"Hello!" I said, happy to see a familiar face.

"Sage! It's so good to see you. I told Darrell I would call and check on you. I hear you may get released today…is that true?"

"Yes, thank God," I said. "I want to go home!"

"Well, I called to pray for you and Darrell. Is he there?"

Darrell walked back into the room at that moment, so I said, "Yes, he's right here."

"What do you want me to pray for?" our pastor asked.

"Well, I need good potassium levels to have the doctor sign my discharge papers."

"Okay then, let's pray."

Our pastor began to ask God that my levels would be perfect, and so I would be able to go home to the comfort of my home and the care of my husband. When we hung up the phone, Darrell and I smiled at each other. I just knew it was going to happen.

And yet, time passed slowly. Three hours later, the phlebotomist came in to draw blood. She told us there was a shift change and my orders were stuck in the change. As she was drawing my blood, I asked her, "Can you make this stat? These levels will determine if I go home today or not. I want to go home."

I sounded pathetic, but by then I didn't care anymore. I was getting wearier with each passing hour.

Another hour passed, and then two, and still no news. I asked Darrell to check on my orders again, and he went to hunt down David. Darrell had his own agenda; he wanted me to go home, but he wanted to leave with an oxygen tank and a walker because I was so frail.

In my mind, I did not think I was frail. The physical therapy folks showed up and brought a few versions of a walker to see which one would suit me. I sat up, got out of bed, and walked the length of the room as they asked, giving it my best effort, not wanting them to report back anything that might delay my discharge.

I had to admit, though, it was difficult to walk the length of the room. I was exhausted. The new room was quite a bit larger than my ICU room.

I did it…I made it to the other side. Then she asked me to walk back.

Good grief, I thought as I fake smiled and said, "Sure!"

The PT tech aligned me with a walker to try, assuring me that it would be best, just in case no one was around to assist me when I was home.

At that moment, Darrell walked in and the PT explained everything she had just told me. He thought it was a good idea.

"Does insurance cover this?" he asked.

"Yes, it does," the tech replied.

She asked us if there were any more questions, and we shook our heads, so she said her goodbyes and left the room.

"How did it go with the nurse?" I asked Darrell.

"Good, he set me up with an O2 guy so we can go home with an oxygen tank today."

"Great, but what about my labs, and when can I leave?"

"Oh, uh, he said he would be in shortly."

"Darrell, isn't that what he said before? Honey, I need to know if I am leaving!"

I was breaking down and frustrated enough to scream.

"I know, I know," said Darrell, trying to calm me down by putting a hand on my arm. "He's working on it, honey."

An hour passed, and finally, David walked in.

"What do you need? I apologize, it has been a crazy zoo out there."

Trying to stay calm, I asked, "David, I need to know if my potassium levels are good, and if so, has the doctor signed my discharge papers?"

"Right," David responded, as if he was reminding himself of my specific situation. "Your levels are great, but I have not heard from your doctor."

I took a breath and said, "David, you know what to do. Please get a hold of her...she promised."

"I'm on it!" he said, and he briskly walked out the door.

Darrell just gazed at me as I played out my master plan. About thirty minutes went by, and there was a knock on the door, followed by a young lady peering in and asking sheepishly,

"May I come in? I'm the MA, and I'm here to remove all the stickers on your body."

"Yes, please, come in," I said.

It sounded favorable that I was going home if they were taking their stickers off my chest. I was sitting near the window, and she walked over to join me.

"I don't even know how many there are."

"Oh, you have about eleven on your chest and abdominal area," the MA responded, as she gently pulled them off. She was very tender and had a pleasant bedside manner.

Darrell left the room; he was looking for the O2 guy. I could tell he was determined to leave only if we had the proper equipment. We already had the walker, so we were just waiting on the O2 now. I was glad he had something else to focus his mind on.

The young MA finished and left the room. I continued to sit near the window. I missed sunshine and earth. I didn't realize how much until I started looking out the window at the blue sky and light, wispy clouds. My thoughts were interrupted by David and Darrell rushing in the door with papers in hand.

He did it. I can't believe it, He did it.

"Well, David, how does it look?" I anxiously asked.

"Here are your discharge papers. Your doctor already left for the day. It's a Friday and folks try to get out of here early, so I called her on her cell phone. She was home and said she forgot, but she went on her computer and signed them right away! I told you, I do not care, if they make a promise I will call them at home to make sure they follow through."

David was gleaming with pride. I felt like he understood my desperation. I was filled with relief.

"Good work, David," I said. "I am truly happy that you are my nurse. Thank you so very much."

"If that is all you need, then I will say goodbye. I wish you luck and a fast recovery, Sage."

I let out a heavy sigh. I did it. But we were still waiting on the O2 guy.

"Darrell, when is he coming?" I asked

"Soon. Are you alright?"

"Not really. I am so exhausted and overtired. When I stare at this floor, the patterns begin to move. My eyes are playing tricks on me…I think I am beyond tired."

"Just a little longer," Darrell said, wrapping his arms around my shoulders.

We waited again. Every minute that went by I could feel myself falling into exhaustion as if it was a deep, black hole threatening to consume me. I stared at the floor, and the patterns were dancing. I had never been so tired that I had hallucinated before.

I need to leave. I need to get home now.

"You said earlier that Sandy might help us with getting home," I said to Darrell. "Can she pick me up, and you can wait for the equipment?"

He looked at me with sympathy and answered, "Sure."

Darrell called Sandy, and then said, "She's on her way."

Coming to Terms with Trauma

The drive home was surreal. My best friend, Sandy, was there near the hospital exit waiting to take me home, while Darrell loaded our car with the home oxygen equipment. He received the equipment shortly after calling Sandy, so he was following us home.

Sandy Schoettle was a special friend and part of a group of executive women who met weekly for Bible study. For five years, I had been the leader of the group. Sandy owns a company called Sea Island Forge, which sells handmade fire kettles. Her husband, Steve, does the iron work. Since COVID, their business has grown exponentially, with families being at home and wanting to create outdoor spaces to safely gather. Sandy came to pick me up in her newly purchased BMW SUV that was dark green with a bit of sparkle in it.

"Damn…look at *this* automobile…," said the orderly, who pushed me like a speed demon down from the room, through the basement garage, and out into the bright sunlight.

"Hey, she worked hard for that," I said. Even though I was delirious, I found the strength to defend my friend from the young man's judgment.

I carefully climbed into the passenger's seat and got situated, reclining the leather seat back far enough to reduce my lightheadedness. Looking at Sandy, I wanted to break down and cry, but I held back the tears, took a hard swallow, and simply said, "It's too emotional. Please, let's not talk."

She nodded her head, seeming to understand the depths of what I had just endured.

"Could we just put on some soft music?" I asked.

She turned on something that sounded like spa music. The car ride was perfectly peaceful. Sandy was an angel for honoring my wishes. I looked outside the window with tears in my eyes, yet I could not feel anything in my body.

I felt very light as if I was not there, almost as if I might be dreaming. It was sunny and bright outside; everything looked so green like an emerald forest. My mind was processing thoughts quickly.

Is this real? What is happening?

We turned down our street. I could feel myself getting happier to crawl in my bed, but the walk from the car to my bedroom would be the longest journey I had taken in a while. It seemed to take forever. One step at a time with a few pauses in between.

Thank God there are no stairs.

Sandy and Darrell helped me into bed. My white sheets felt like marshmallows compared to the hospital sheets I had been in for almost two weeks. I felt comfort wash over me.

I'm home. I'm safe.

I fell asleep quickly.

I was up at 9:30 p.m. and Darrell brought me a little chicken soup. He stayed out in the living room with the dogs so I wouldn't be disturbed. I tried to fall asleep again, yet I awoke choking and coughing.

It was 11:21 p.m. I lay there, unable to fall asleep. I waited. I listened to the wind chimes, and the wind rustling leaves outside my window. I sat up in the bed, assessing how I felt, and my first thought was,

Yuck! I need a bath. Oh my, I have not bathed in 2 weeks.
I texted Darrell.

"Can you give me a bath?"

Silence…

"Can you take me potty?"

I thought maybe a bath was too much at midnight. Truth is, he's not a nurse, and we have never had a situation like this in our marriage. I had no idea what he was willing to do.

The door flew open as Darrell rushed into my room, like Joey from *Friends*.

"Do you want a bath?" he asked.

"Yes, please, is that ok?"

He went straight into action, drawing me a bath at midnight. My skin was leathery and had a waxy appearance. I also had a lot of acne on my back and it was itchy. Darrell only filled up the tub with a small amount of water—he didn't want me slipping—but I remember how wonderful the clean water felt on my body. Darrell was usually very verbal, but I was thankful he withheld any comments. He washed me and helped me get back into bed.

I woke up again at 2 a.m. and 4 a.m. My nervous system was overactive. I continued to wake up every couple of hours not knowing where I was, feeling anxious. Then realizing I was home, I talked myself into breathing and calming down. My mind and my body were on two different
pages.

The next morning I texted Darrell to help me use the bathroom. I slept on the left side of the bed; the bathroom door was only five feet from the bed. Once in the bathroom, it was another eight feet to the toilet. This was daunting, since it was way farther than the hospital room I had been navigating.

Darrell was sleeping in the living room with the dogs to keep them from jumping on me. I was so weak and easily winded, but as Darrell supported me on my left side, we walked into the bathroom and I stopped in front of the mirror on the right and took inventory of myself in the morning light. I was down sixteen pounds, had lost a large percentage of muscle mass, and there were bruises and IV puncture wounds all over my body. My face was gaunt and pale.

It was shocking to see myself. I understood the outward physical healing process, but I had not anticipated the amount of emotional and mental healing that I needed.

For five nights in a row, I woke up with a violent choking and coughing spell at 11:21 p.m. I had no idea why this was happening, but I found it difficult to get back to sleep. Often I would just lay there quietly. By the fifth morning, I decided to ask Darrell about it.

I shuffled my way to the dining room table, where Darell was milling around the kitchen making coffee.

"Darrell, do you know what the significance of 11:21 p.m. might be? I keep waking up coughing and choking at that exact time every night."

Darrell dried his hands, and I could almost see his thoughts churning.

"Are you sure you're ready to hear this?"

"Yes! Please tell me," I said, almost begging.

Darrell grabbed a stack of scribbled papers bound together with an oversized paper clip and sat down on the chair beside me with a heavy exhale.

Flipping through the papers, he arrived at the answer.

"11:21 is the exact time they had to intubate you the second time. The first ventilator was taken out on a Saturday night…" his voice trailed off, and then…

"We were all so happy that you were coming off the vent…I was calling everyone and telling them that our prayers had been answered and you were gonna be okay. But then I got the call that you couldn't seem to breathe on your own, and they had to intubate you again. It was 11:21 when they did it."

I had no memory of this. I was moved that Darrell knew exactly what had happened and when. It was the first time I realized that he might have trauma of his own from experiencing me being so close to death.

"Oh my gosh, Darrell. Somehow my brain knows this happened even though I have no memory of it."

So, this is what PTSD is like.

"I think my nervous system is in fight or flight from all of this."

"Yeah, I bet it is." Darrell breathed in deeply and sighed again, like he needed to get some things off his chest.

"I'll tell you this, Sage, the day I left you at the hospital, I was a wreck. It just all set in that I might lose you. When we were at the hospital at first, I was telling myself, 'Sage is strong, she has this, my wife can get through just about anything.' But when you called me that last time before they put you under and you said, 'It doesn't look good, it's actually bad, really bad,' I fell apart. I came home, and cried, and paced, and drank. I thought, 'Oh my God, what am I gonna do? I can't lose her. This can't be happening.'"

"Oh, Darrell…" I grabbed his hand and squeezed it.

"You know how hard this pension thing has been on me… wanting to be done and move to the island with you, and then the company deciding to renegotiate it, and now I can't retire… and then the idea of losing you too…"

"I know, Darrell…"

"…It just all came crashing down on me. I called Wayne that night, and we talked for two hours while I drank one beer after another. Finally, I was so tired, I slumped in the chair in the living room and fell asleep, but I woke up early. My first thought was, 'Oh God, this is not a nightmare, this is my life, I have to do something.'

So I went to the beach to talk to God. I walked until the sun came up, and I felt like I could finally breathe. My dad called and offered to come out and help, but of course I tried to be the tough guy and told him I could handle it. But I was a mess."

"You did call your dad and ask him to come, right?" I asked. I knew my father-in-law and his wife had been with Darrell during my hospitalization.

"Yeah, I did later that afternoon. I asked him how soon he could get here, and he said they would be on the earliest flight out. I just needed the support. He and Barb came, and you know, she's a retired nurse, so it was good having her here too. They both helped me so much, Sage.

Dad was the most sensitive and caring he's ever been. I think he was really worried about me. He also helped me get serious about taking care of things around here. Barb was on the calls with me to the hospital, and she'd help me ask the right questions and then translate all the terminology. I had no idea what they were talking about half the time."

"Wait, when did they leave?" I asked, still trying to grasp basic concepts of time.

"The day you came home. I wanted them to stay, but it made sense. Barb realized you would just need a quiet place to rest. In fact, the day I took them, I was halfway to the airport and I got the call that they were taking you to another room, which meant I could finally visit you. Dad said, 'Drop us off here, we'll Uber the rest of the way.' I didn't do it, but it was sweet of them to offer."

"How did you keep all of these notes on my progress?" I asked, looking over at his notes on the table and the many pages filled with his scribbled handwriting.

"I called the hospital every morning at 4 a.m. and 9 a.m. for an update. I found out that the operator is my colleague's former assistant, so when we realized it, she would connect me right through to the nurse in ICU. After the 4 a.m. call, I called Joyce

next door, because she's up early and she's such a great listener…
it helped just to process everything out loud.

After that, I would make my coffee and go straight to the
beach and walk every morning for like an hour. It just kind of
grounded me, because I was so emotional. After that, I would call
Dr. Erwin to let him know what was going on and see if I needed
to ask any questions. He helped me so much, Sage. I wouldn't
have known anything about the medical stuff they were telling
me, but he was right there, explaining everything to me."

"Wow, what a godsend," I answered.

"Yeah, I know. They wanted to do that experimental
procedure on you where they take your blood out and spin it and
then put it back in. They've been doing it all over the U.S., but
Dr. Erwin said to refuse it; he didn't want you having it done, so
I told them no."

"Yeah, I sat with that stupid PICC line in my neck for
nothing…" I replied, not trying to hide my irritation.

"Oh, and I guess now's a good time to tell you, I went
ahead and told everybody what you were going through."

"…Everybody?" I asked.

"Well, I made sure all of your circles were notified…you
know, your friends, your work, the church, the neighborhood,
and they all kept updates going out on Facebook so people could
know the latest on how you were doing. When I would get the 4
a.m. update, I would text Robyn with the news, and she would
post it on Facebook. And then Pastor David would post it on his
own page."

"Wow. Ok…I'm just very private, you know, Darrell. I don't want to be a burden and have others worry about me."

"I know," Darrell said. "But Sage, people understand that you were really sick. And I'll make sure you only have visitors when you're up to it."

"Thank you. Thank you for being here for me. I'm so tired, Darrell."

"Well, why don't you lie down on the couch for a bit? I'll bring you some water."

I shuffled over to the couch, eased myself down, pulled my fleece blanket up to my neck and closed my eyes, trying to block out all the anxiety about what was ahead.

Everyone knew.

Of course Darrell would tell everyone. If he would have had my phone, he would have called everyone on my contact list. I felt exposed and vulnerable, and I didn't like the idea that so many people were feeling pity for me. I wanted to continue being the Sage I brought to the world—strong, giving, and an expert in my field.

Instead, I felt small, weak, and frail; how I would get back to myself was impossible to even imagine. The only word that came to my mind was *surrender*.

Surrender to this healing, Sage. Surrender to this process.

The most difficult thing to surrender was my work. As a self-employed concierge practitioner, I had a business to run, not just a job where I could take a leave of absence and it was someone else's responsibility to fill in the gaps. Not only that, but people expected things from me to help them. There was the constant pressure of expectation, and I struggled internally to let that go and accept that my only job was to recover.

No one is expecting anything from me. No one's judging. And if they are, they don't know the whole picture, and they will find out, and it'll be okay.

Once again, my mind was on two different pages. Part of me was still wanting to push and continue serving, and the other part knew I couldn't even take care of myself.

Even Dogs Hate Covid

During the ten days I was in the hospital, my three dogs were constantly looking for me, checking the front door, sitting in my office during the day, and being extremely clingy, according to Darrell.

They are normally affectionate with him, but when I was gone, it was way more than usual. They knew Darrell was acting strange, and they rallied around him, even when he was so grief-stricken he forgot to feed them a couple times.

The second night I was hospitalized, Darrell sat on the kitchen floor crying. They all came around and sat with him, attending to him in his sadness.

The day I got home, they went ballistic. They could see me coming in, and Darrell locked them outside to allow me safe passage to the bedroom, but they were not pleased with the arrangement. They are all used to being in the bed with me, whether Darrell is home or not.

After my first couple of hours of sleep, we decided that the dogs could come in one at a time to say hello. Braccio came in first (the middle child), and he was spooked by the oxygen tank. He licked me while at the same time looking around as if to ask, "What is all this stuff?"

Next, Gianna came in, being her normal, puppyish self, jumping, licking, spinning around, and generally overwhelming me with her energy. She didn't stay long, but she was thrilled to see me.

Finally, we decided that my old girl, Cara Mia, would come in and sleep with me. She jumped up on the bed, where I was propped up on two pillows.

Walking up to me carefully, she placed her nose on my nose, gave me a tiny little lick, then turned around in a complete about-face. She walked over to the other side of the bed and plopped down, giving the longest sigh I'd ever heard from a dog.

It was like she had been holding her breath for ten days.

I know how you feel, Cara Mia. I've been holding my breath too. But I'm home now. We can both rest.

Recovering Me

My life was practically at a stand still. My mornings were spent slowly walking to the dining room table where Darrell and I read the Bible together.

As I continued sitting there, Darrell scurried around the kitchen making me breakfast and tidying up the kitchen.

We went through the mail together, and I realized that Darrell had depended on me for so many things—taking care of the bills, the dogs, and everything related to the house. He had been lost when I was in the hospital. We never had a conversation about when the water bill was due; I took care of it. Darrell didn't even know where I kept the spare key to the house.

Darrell was in daily contact with Pastor David, who prayed for me on the phone, and also on Facebook Live. Dr. Erwin came over to check on me after I was home a few days, and he knew me well enough to know I wasn't a very good patient. I wanted to get this recovery business over so I could get back to work. When Dr. Erwin was visiting one morning, he reached over to the side table by the couch and picked up the remote.

"See this TV, Sage?" He was trying to be funny, but I didn't laugh.

"Get acquainted with all the TV shows."

"I don't even know what to watch...I don't even watch TV," I said in a flat tone.

He picked up my remote and pointed it at the TV.

"Here's Netflix. Get an account. Do you have Apple TV?"

"Yes...I think."

"Check out *Ted Lasso*."

I looked at Darrell. "Ted what?"

Dr. Erwin looked back at me until my eyes met his.

"*Ted Lasso*. It's a great show. Listen, it's gonna take you three to six weeks just for you to walk to the counter and stand there to get a glass of water and walk back. That's okay, Sage."

"What?" I asked.

He sat down on the loveseat and his voice softened.

"You were in the hospital for eleven days, Sage. You were in a coma for eight days. You weren't resting. You were on a treadmill running for your life. That's why you're almost twenty pounds down. That's why you're weak. You beat the odds and were discharged just a few days after coming out of the coma. You really should have been in the hospital for eight weeks, as bad as you were. Now you're gonna need three to six months to recover and maybe a year to get back to your old, feisty self."

"I don't have that kinda time, Doc."

"Oh, but you do, my friend."

He wasn't backing down, and I didn't like being on this side of the doctor-patient relationship.

"Listen, Sage, what happened to you was intense, and your body has fought a hard fight. Your job now is to give it the time it needs to heal. Be patient with yourself and let Darrell do the heavy lifting, ok?"

I sighed. This wasn't me. I didn't like feeling exhausted, wrung out, dependent, and incapable.

"Ok, Doc. I don't think I really have a choice, do I?"

"Not really. But attitude is very important in recovery. You know that."

"Hmm," I answered, knowing he was right but not wanting to hear it.

The post-COVID fatigue was ferocious. I learned that much of it has to do with how COVID recalibrates your heart rate to be in the 80s, 90s, or even 100s. Darrell took my vitals and checked my oxygen levels daily. My heart rate stayed in the 90s for four weeks. Eventually, it decreased.

Dr. Tina was good to her word and came over every other day. She gave me chiropractic care and aromatherapy with key specific essential oils. My body had been through so much, and it was on edge—even defensive— toward her attempts to give me an adjustment.

Since I was 19 years old, I had been getting chiropractic adjustments. But due to the trauma I endured, it felt like we were starting from scratch. She would patiently adjust me, and I would feel good for a couple of hours and then go right back to feeling terrible again. My body wouldn't hold an alignment.

But Dr. Tina persisted, driving many miles out of her way several times a week to work with me. I explained to her that I couldn't sleep through the night because my body was still in flight or flight mode. It became clear I was holding a lot of anger toward the hospital staff for intubating me a second time. My thoughts were along the lines of…

What…you couldn't do it right the first time? What's wrong with you people?

Dr. Tina gave me specific instructions to take fractionated oil with essential lavender oil and put it on each wrist, as if I was applying perfume, and then to have Darrell rub the lavender oil up and down my spine. I was also supposed to speak these words out loud.

"I forgive them. I am not in harm's way anymore. They did the best job they could. They cannot hurt me again. I forgive them, and I am okay. I will be fine."

Every night for five nights I said those words while Darrell rubbed the lavender oil on me until I finally slept through the night. It took over a week of treatments for my body to register that it was not in danger anymore.

[Ever since this experience, I've been telling my patients who also struggle with post-COVID PTSD to do the same thing, and the results have been astounding.]

During my recovery, I was overwhelmed by the outpouring of love by our community. Our home looked like a floral shop; flowers were delivered daily. I loved them, all of them.

Because of Darrell reaching out and being the expressive man he is, more and more folks found out about what had happened and sent cards, food, and caring messages.

There was a food train set up online, and Darrell set a Yeti cooler on our front porch, which was filled with meals each and every day. Darrell was relieved to have the meals generously donated, as he felt obligated to feed me three times a day plus snacks. He was determined to have me gain my strength back before he was forced to go back to work. Darrell was on Emergency Family Leave for two months. I was unemployed and received no income during my recovery. I was not worried; I knew God had me in His arms. My faith was so strong. We both had a surreal sense of peace.

Looking back on those few months, it was as if Darrell and I were able to hit the pause button on life. Time moved slowly, and we were upheld by the love of God and of His people.

After our morning routine, we would discuss and process the events that had happened, and it became a sweet time of closeness between us.

"I was worried about you that day we left the hospital, Sage."

Darrell was sitting forward leaning on the table, his chin in his left hand, while I sat in my chair with half of my pancake breakfast still left on the plate. I wasn't someone who normally started the day with pancakes, but Darrell made it a point to make me whatever food I was craving at the moment. I ate cheesecake, chocolate cake, barbecue beef, and all the things I didn't allow myself in ordinary life.

"Oh yeah, why's that?" I asked.

"Well, you were starting to hallucinate pretty badly. I knew you hadn't slept, but do you remember when the oxygen guy came in to show us the machine and how to use it right before Sandy picked you up?"

I thought back and could only remember being more exhausted than I had ever been before in my life. "Not really, I was out of it."

"Well, when the guy left, you said, 'Darrell, that's Charles Barkley...the NBA player.'"

I snickered, vaguely remembering the scene. "I was on a lot of Fentanyl."

"Yeah, I guess so," Darrell continued, "You made up this whole story about how Charles Barkley must work in Brunswick now and have his own company, and no one knows who he really is, so he's working incognito."

"Wow...that's pretty imaginative."

We both laughed, and it felt good.

"I remember Sandy driving me home and taking this weird way that I didn't recognize at all," I recalled. "She entered the Causeway from a different street than she usually goes and said 'It's safer this way.' I was too tired to even comment. I was so detached from everything...I wasn't in the world yet."

"God, Sage, I was just so happy you were home. I felt so much relief; I just knew you would get better if we could get you home."

"Yeah, I think I knew that, too. Darrell, I can't even believe how horrible I looked when I got home. My hair was gross, I stunk, I hadn't bathed in almost two weeks. I hadn't plucked my eyebrows or cut my nails..."

"You did have a lot going on there..." Darrell's voice trailed off.

"But Sage," he leaned in and grabbed my hand, "you were the most beautiful thing I had ever seen."

I shook my head. I was one lucky lady to be loved like this. In truth, our time together at that table became the most intimate time we had ever spent in our fifteen years of marriage. Darrell wasn't distracted with work, and neither was I. God was present. We were talking about God, praying together, and our partnership wasn't just about getting things done.

It could have gone either way; we could have let the crisis drive us apart, but we were both making the choice to lean in toward God and each other. Darrell stepped up and stepped in, made himself present to me and to what God wanted to accomplish in that time.

It's strange. As I reflect on that time we had together, I miss it. I was so frail and weak and incapable of doing basic tasks, but I miss the closeness we experienced, Darrell and I. I wished so badly that he could retire, and we could continue our latter years of marriage together living in one place, building on that intimacy we cultivated during my recovery.

I experienced a snapshot with Darrell of what it felt like during my encounter with Jesus. When I was in a coma and Jesus appeared, I felt completely embraced in pure love. I was whole, with nothing missing or broken, while I was in His presence.

Coming back into my body was the ultimate disappointment, because in our bodies, we don't know that kind of experiential love all the time. We crave it and we look for it in all kinds of places, many of them unhealthy.

On this side of heaven, experiencing the presence and love of God requires the discipline of setting time and space to quiet ourselves, get into His Word, and pray.

On this side of heaven, people expect us to show up for work, fulfill our responsibilities, which are good things, but also can serve to distract us from the awareness of God's presence.

God provided Darrell and me a window of two months to experience Him without the pressures of life pressing in, and the benefit was a deepened level of friendship and intimacy between us we had never experienced.

My usual routine before COVID was to sit in the morning with my coffee and read my Bible, and then spend some time journaling. In the beginning of my recovery, I was unable to write at all, and even the television was too stimulating for me. So I would read my Bible and then just sit. I would sit for hours, until finally I made my way back to the couch.

Sometimes I would talk for hours with Darrell about my grandparents and about what my grandmother said to me while I was in the coma. It was a time to process deep emotions while my body was too weak to keep my usual busy pace. It was also a time to allow Darrell to process his experience of coming close to losing me.

"Sage, when the nurse called me that day and asked me for your phone passcode because you wanted music, I was overwhelmed. I knew at that point you were gonna make it. You know, they didn't give me any promises about how you would come out of the coma…whether you would have any brain damage or if you would still be *you*. But when I heard you wanted music, I knew you were still in there."

I smiled. "Yeah, you know how I am about my music…I have to have it on all day long."

"Oh, and get this. I called Sandy right away and told her about the music, and we were screaming in joy. She got it. She knew what it meant. Sandy was at the hospital with Steve that same day…they were getting their vaccines. Sandy said she looked up at the ceiling from down in the clinic and thought, 'Sage needs her music.' Two hours later, I called her and told her about the music."

"Woah…that's crazy. We were having some kind of telepathy there."

Darrell filled me in on all the happenings during the time I had lost – about the first day we were able to FaceTime and how that same day his dad and Barb got all dressed up for St. Patrick's Day. They took him out for a beer to celebrate his dad's birthday. It was good for Darrell to get out and take his mind off everything for a few hours.

After a couple of weeks, when I finally worked up the strength to write, I began journaling again. As I scanned back through previous entries, I realized my journal was mostly about me controlling the narrative of my life—I wrote about what I would do that day, how I thought things should work out.

After COVID, I became more curious about what narrative God had for me. I began asking more open-ended questions in my journal.

What do you need me to do today? Who do you need me to speak to and pour love into today?

I could feel a deep shift in my heart. I was becoming more surrendered, less frantic, less driven by the needs and expectations of people. I was living—maybe for the first time ever—like a child of God. He became my guide and the director of my days, and it felt freeing.

Darrell received a voicemail that a friend from work wanted to set up a GoFundMe account for us. His friend insisted, because all the guys at work Darrell had helped over and over wanted to take the opportunity to help us in return. We were very moved by the gesture. The moment it was launched, the funds poured in.

"God is showing us trust and surrender," I said to Darrell, as he sat there with his bright blue eyes filled with tears.

The funds paid for our living expenses and kept us in our home. We were okay.

Post—Covid Protocol

After COVID, my life was about pockets of time. My days were scheduled with physical therapy, doctor's appointments, and eating. Nutrition along with my supplement protocol became critical to my healing process. My body needed help detoxing all the chemicals from IV medications and the cellular and tissue damage from the virus.

I took a month and a half off from work, just to heal and regain my strength. My nutrition included dark, leafy greens daily with protein; organic chicken, fish, and grass-fed beef. I used ghee with turmeric daily, which is clarified butter; it is lactose and casein-free and has powerful healing properties. My post-COVID supplement protocol included:

Phase 1:
Andrographis Immuneplex Congaplex
Sesame Seed Oil
Pneumotrophin PMG Probiotic
Magnesium
Zinc
Veg-E nutrition shake daily

Phase 2:
Methyl folate
Glutathione
Vitamin E
Arginine
Multi/Mineral
Cat's Claw

Burdock

Fish oil

(many of these products were from Standard Process)

The roles Darrell and I were used to were no longer possible. Darrell became my cook, domestic engineer, caretaker, and coach. He took a 14"x20" whiteboard and with thick markers wrote down the days of the week and what exercises I was required to do. Monday, Wednesday, and Friday were squats and sit-ups. Tuesday and Thursday were walks up and down the stairs. I resisted the stairs—they were the hardest. And the breathing treatment. The Incentive Spirometer, which was supposed to expand my lungs by helping me breathe deeper, was something I despised.

When I would get to the point where I could do the exercises on the board, he would give me harder ones. Darrell was gentle, kind, and encouraging. I vacillated between resenting him and loving him for pushing me like he did. By week three, we went to the gym. He would give me three exercises, and I would do them obediently—most days.

After about two weeks of being home from the hospital, people began asking if they could come to the house and see me. Darrell and I discussed having visitors before anyone came over, because I did not have the energy to engage in conversation for very long in the early days of my recovery.

One of my first visitors was Justin, an assistant pastor at our church. One of the things I had made standard practice in my work was to give chiropractic adjustments to pastors and their wives for free. It has been one way I can give back to the local church, and Justin came in regularly as a patient.

Justin had been a rock for Darrell during my hospitalization. Each morning he would text to get the daily update on my progress. Then he would bring the update to the church staff meeting so they could pray for the day's specific concerns.

One morning Darrell forgot to text the update, and twenty minutes later, there was Justin, checking in to make sure everything was okay. The faithfulness of friends like Justin can never be repaid or forgotten.

Others visited around the same time, including Sandy and Steve. Sandy let me know that the Bible study group I led had continued meeting to pray for me, which meant the world to me. I was always the one rallying the group together, sending reminders and doing the prep work. It made me happy to know someone else had stepped up, and they continued meeting without me.

Saint Simons Island has a large retired population, and although we were hit hard in 2020, 2021 proved to be our deadliest year overall. In January of 2021, Glynn County reported 137 COVID deaths since the beginning of the pandemic. However, by the end of October, that number climbed to 300 due to the Delta strand that appeared in late summer.

It was a devastating time for so many families in our community, and the isolation and fear of spreading the virus made it more difficult for us to comfort one another.

I found it interesting that several visitors told stories about other COVID patients they knew, most of whom were still in the hospital fighting for their lives. I'm not sure if they struggled to find something to say, or if it was their feeble attempt to make me feel better about having survived. I didn't know how to process these stories; I still don't know how to process them. I have no understanding as to why God allowed me to survive while others did not.

Clarity and Closure

Once it was time to go back to work, I knew that I had to take a hard look at my schedule and begin setting boundaries—like learning the art of practicing *no*. (I had a therapist whose mantra became my own: "No is a complete sentence.")

It wasn't the first time I had done this, and I knew it could be done. I also knew life had a way of pulling me right back on the treadmill once I stepped off. When I was practicing in Tampa, I would occasionally take trips to Italy, which would serve to slow me down and correct my frantic pace. When I returned, I was rejuvenated and would change my work template to include a three-hour lunch break.

Since I lived four blocks from work, I was able to go home, walk the dog, make a big, healthy salad for lunch, and take a nap. As time progressed, I noticed myself stacking more errands into that time—maybe because it seemed like everyone else was running around while I was taking a siesta. Eventually I would find myself right back where I started: burnt out and overworked.

Before I got sick, I had been pushing hard to meet the rising demands with COVID, but also because I had a tendency to overlook my own needs while busily caring for others. I needed to slow down. It wasn't my job to save the world, even though it felt like the world was knocking at my door for help. COVID had grown my business internationally, so I had patients calling from Romania, Portugal, and Bangkok in the early morning hours. I had to remember I was only one person. More than anything, I wanted to follow the instructions I received while in my coma: *practice the gift without becoming distracted.*

I knew I needed to delegate some things, so I started there. I delegated my social media and marketing. I had been working two and a half days in the clinic and three full days consulting patients from home.

The online nutrition consults meant I was sitting in front of a computer for eight hours a day. I needed to build more margin into my life. So I cut down my clinical hours to two half-days per week, and only took four to five nutrition clients at a time. These weren't easy decisions, but I felt I had been given a second chance, and I was committed to managing my stress and staying healthy.

It was mid-October, 2022, more than eighteen months since making it out of the COVID ICU. The air was unusually cool for that time of year, a welcome change in a climate that is split in half between pleasantly mild and brutally hot.

I decided to visit the fourth floor of the hospital to get some closure; to talk with my nurses and thank them for the care they gave me. I had been back to an outpatient clinic at the same facility for a checkup in late 2021, but I had not been in the main hospital since the day I was wheeled out and helped into Sandy's car.

I felt nervous, unsettled even, as I made my way out of the bright blue autumn sky into the dinginess of the hospital lobby. The medicinal smell brought me right back to the previous March when I felt like a prisoner inside its sterile walls. The elevator was empty, and I was grateful for a quiet ride alone.

Following the signs to the ICU and approaching the desk, I noticed there were construction signs. The girl behind the desk was familiar, I recognized her face. She was a pretty, African American lady with a medium build, her hair pulled tightly back in a bun, her smile soft and kind.

My mouth was parched, and I felt a little light-headed. I launched right in.

"Hi. I know a patient who was here during COVID, and I was wondering if I could thank some of the nurses who helped her recover."

"Oh, ok. Who was the patient?"

"Uh…I'd rather not say."

"OK, sure. Then, um, who were the nurses?"

"Well, there was Bailey and Joe…"

"Is Joe the respiratory nurse?"

"No…he was a regular nurse."

"Oh, well then I don't think he's here anymore. Bailey is also not here anymore. Lots of nurses who were here during that time have either moved on or left the profession altogether. It was a stressful time, ya know…"

"Yes, but…wow. They're all gone? Even Michelle?

"Yes, I remember Michelle. She moved back upstate, I think. If you'd like, you could give me the patient's first name, and I could ask around and see if anyone remembers him or her."

I was too overwhelmed to continue skirting the truth.

"It was me. I was the patient."

Front-desk girl nodded and put her head down before speaking again. It was as if the scene flashed in her mind.

"I was here, I ran this desk," she said, her tone steady like a soldier who was a first-hand witness in a war zone. "But I never left this area. I had to stay up here at the front."

"Can you take me to the COVID unit?" I asked.

"No," she replied, "it is closed off and being demolished. It's around that corner; we called it, 'The Pocket.'"

That's right, I thought the nurses used that word to describe our area. I remember it being like a 'cul-de-sac' area. The rooms made a semicircle and I remember my room was the second on the left. But I will never see it again. It's gone.

I peeked my head around the doorway, and I saw it—a big, makeshift wall with a door covered in plastic and a printed sign attached: "DO NOT ENTER…HARD HAT ONLY… CONSTRUCTION ZONE."

"Wow, it really is closed," I said quietly, to myself.

"Yep," said the front-desk girl. She was very matter-of-fact, and I assumed that's why she was able to stay while everyone else left.

Thanking her for her time, I made my way back to the elevator. I could feel my heart racing; I had to catch my breath. Disappointment washed over me, and my throat tightened as tears welled up.

So this was it? We're moving on now? We're just trying to go on like it never happened? It did happen, didn't it?

Brain fog and a heavy sadness in my chest settled in as I made my way out into the parking lot.

The Pocket had been demoed, it was no more. The nurses were gone.

Game over.

I knew I was being triggered, but I was too angry to care. I went there for closure, to see if all the visions in my head matched what I had actually experienced. To look into the eyes of someone who had seen me at my lowest moment and feel some kind of connection over the trauma we all went through with this horrendous virus.

Now I was faced with a hard reality. People wanted to forget about it, clear away the evidence, and move on.

I couldn't do that.

In the days that followed, I thought a lot about how I could do my part to honor the suffering brought on by a pandemic that affected so many lives, including my own. I brought my anger, frustration, and trauma to God in prayer. Gradually, I began to see that the best thing I could do was to share my story.

Over time, with more healing, it became my mission to share my experience as often as possible, despite my private nature. I shared it at church, with friends, with colleagues, and I made a commitment in my heart to share it in a book.

I believe this book needed to be written, and the words flowed out into my journal over the course of many mornings during recovery (usually at around 4 a.m.).

This pandemic has touched many lives on so many levels. I hope my story touches others with a loving tenderness. For those of you who suffered sickness or loss because of COVID, please know you are not alone.

A few words from Pastor Justin

During this global pandemic, if you have had the loss of loved ones, or you yourself have experienced the tragedy of COVID, let me say a few words of prayer and comfort:

My hope and prayer for anybody who reads this book is for you to find hope and encouragement. Nobody journeyed through this global pandemic without experiencing many different emotions of fear, anger, stress, sadness, grief etc… We all learned life is a gift. It is fragile, precious, unpredictable, and we as humans ultimately lack being in control.

We read this book remembering the events of this global pandemic and how COVID changed this world overnight. Many of us know others personally who traveled this road with COVID and tragically have lost their life or are still fighting the effects of COVID. Some of you are reading this having experienced the same fears and uncertainty Sage experienced.

Sage's story is for you to know we all traveled this road together and we are not alone.

God shows up when everything is great, but his promise is to be with us in our pain and when it seems all is lost. He lets us know we will have troubles, but He will see us through (John 16:33).

Dear Heavenly Father,
I pray for every soul who reads this book. I pray they will receive hope, find peace, and be encouraged. May you move in hearts so we would know your goodness. You promise to be with us in all things

through all circumstances never giving up on us. Would you come close and change us, so that we can offer this same hope to other. In the name of the Father, the Son, and the Holy Spirit. Amen.

Justin Davidson, Spiritual Formation Minister of Community Church, Saint Simons Island, GA

About the Author

Dr. Sage Campione is a Chiropractor and Functional Medicine practitioner. She has lived a life of service, beginning when she was a medic in the United States Army. Her passion for helping others led her to a career in Chiropractic, graduating in 1997 from Life University in Atlanta, GA with post-graduate training in Integrative Medicine from the University of Arizona. An understanding of the mind-body connection led her to broaden her scope of expertise. Her training includes Ayurvedic Medicine, Wellness, Nutrition, and Functional Medicine. She truly believes an integrated lifestyle will help you sustain a quality, healthy life.

She has been married to Darrell Dent since 2007. They have known each other since 3rd grade when then met in Confraternity of Christian Doctrine, or CCD, class. Darrell has a daughter from a previous marriage, Peyton. She was born in 1999.

When the journey started she had three pups, but now there is just Gianna. Dr. Campione's passions are traveling, learning, exploring, and having rich friendships.

She attends Community Church on a regular basis. The support on Saint Simons Island continues.

Her favorite quote is, "If you think you can, you can." And her second favorite is, "Don't put it off until tomorrow, do it today, because we do not know what tomorrow brings."

Published by

Marigold Press Books
Relationship focused, independent publisher
sharing stories of hope.

Marigold Press was created to build a legacy by sharing stories of hope
and magnifying the voices of women. Founders Emra Smith and Rebekah
McLeod saw a gap in the industry that left budding authors wandering
and aimless. Their intention is to provide a relationship focused publishing
experience where they guide authors through the entire process from
idea inception to published book to marketing and more.

Visit Us
www.marigoldpressbooks.org

Instagram
@marigoldpressbooks

Email
marigoldpressbooks@gmail.com